MICHAEL JACKSON

1958-2009

WISE PUBLICATIONS
PART OF THE MUSIC SALES GROUP

London / New York / Los Angeles / Paris / Sydney / Copenhagen / Berlin / Madrid / Tokyo / Hong Kong

STAR 20p
WWW.DAILYSTAR.CO.UK 20p
FRIDAY JUNE 26, 2009
GET TODAY'S DAILY EXPRESS FOR JUST 20p
Simply hand the voucher on P34 to your newsagent

TRAGIC STAR DIES OF HEART ATTACK

MICHAEL JACKSON DEAD AT 50

SHOCK: Medics fight in vain to save star

■ by ANTHONY WALTON

KING of Pop Michael Jackson dropped dead of a heart attack last night.

The 50-year-old superstar collapsed at his Los Angeles home and paramedics were unable to revive him.

Weeping fans immediately began paying tribute as the music legend's sudden death sent "a tidal wave of shock" around the world.

Tribute edition: Pages 2,3,4 & 5

---

www.mingpao.com
報明
2009·06·27
Michael Jackson 逝世
A1 A4 A6

死前疑打嗎啡
米高積遜
猝然謝幕
女聖墊姦不良死 父母被捕

1958-2009

DAILY Mirror
Friday June 26, 2009
REAL NEWS.. REAL ENTERTAINMENT 45p

JACKO DEAD

King of Pop killed by heart attack at 50

By GREIG BOX TURNBULL

THE world was in shock last night after Michael Jackson died of a massive heart attack at the age of just 50.

Medics were called to the King of Pop's Los Angeles home after he suddenly collapsed and stopped breathing.

The pop singer - whose career had been marred by scandal - was rushed to hospital where doctors desperately tried to resuscitate him but he died at 2.26pm local time. Fans around the world were stunned by the death of pop's biggest star. By early this morning, hundreds were gathering outside the hospital - meant to learn.

Close friend Uri Geller said: "I'm absolutely shocked and devastated."

Jacko's distraught mum Katherine and his brothers had rushed to the hospital to be at his side.

TURN TO PAGE 3

▲ PANIC Jacko is rushed to hospital last night

MICHAEL JACKSON

1958-2009

By Chris Charlesworth

The first time I saw Michael Jackson was in November, 1972. He was 14 years old but looked younger somehow, perhaps because he was the smallest member of the Jackson 5 and his four brothers towered over him as they went through their paces before an astonished, media-only, audience at the Talk Of The Town in London's Leicester Square. He might have been small but he grabbed all the attention, and all of us in that small audience that day will remember what we saw for the rest of our lives.

I was sat opposite the DJ John Peel with whom I was on nodding terms in those days. We watched the J5 show together with mounting astonishment and I distinctly remember that during 'I'll Be There' Michael span around so that his back was to the audience, a 180 degree turn, then sang the line: 'Just look over your shoulder, girl' and he did exactly that, looking at us, the audience, over his shoulder. He then span around again to face us with such exhilarating panache that Peely and I looked at one another with our mouths wide open, shocked almost, but recognising instantly and with absolute certainty that the little boy on stage was such that comes along only once in a lifetime.

ichael
ckson,
g of
, dies
d 50

could not revive him

wasn't just that he sang with a maturity well beyond his years or that he danced like Nijinsky.
was a combination of all that and something more, some indescribable flash of innate genius that
arked him out as 'the chosen one', in a world of his own.

terwards, back at *Melody Maker's* offices on Fleet Street, I wrote the following words:
Michael Jackson is poised to be the biggest coloured show business sensation the world has ever
nown. Put his name in neon lights, splash him across the front page, write it in the sky, tell
verybody you know... Michael will be a brighter star than anything the Milky Way can serve up."

vas right, of course, but I can't claim much credit. It was obvious to anyone with eyes and ears
at Michael Jackson was on the brink of a fabulous career. What I didn't know – and nor did anyone
se – was that this career would turn him into a freak show, the weirdest man in show business,
d that he would never, ever, grow up.

Michael was born on 29 August 1958, the seventh of nine children of Joe and Katherine Jackson, who lived in Gary, Indiana, at the southern tip of Lake Michigan where this huge family of six boys and three girls was squeezed into a two-bedroom house. Joe, a steel worker, was a strict disciplinarian and Michael would later claim that his father often beat him. Despite his precocious talents as a singer and dancer he was chronically shy, and would remain so throughout his life.

This shyness disappeared every time he climbed on stage, and when he was six he joined a group made up from his siblings, Jackie, Tito, Jermaine and Marlon, who called themselves The Jackson Brothers. The youngest Jackson brother, Randy, would join later while two of his three sisters, La Toya and Janet, would go on to have successful singing careers in their own right. At the age of eight, Michael assumed lead vocals, and the group's name was changed to the Jackson 5.

Under Joe's tuition the Jackson 5 began to perform at clubs and burlesque joints around Gary and in 1968 were seen by the singer Gladys Knight who brought them to the attention of Berry Gordy, the boss of Motown Records in Detroit. "He sang his songs with such feeling," said Gordy, "such inspiration and pain – like he had experienced everything he was singing about."

星島日報
SING TAO DAILY
sinotao.com
2009年6月27日（星期六）
港幣六元正
己丑年年閏五月初五日
定價 25-28℃

送《超級睇樓王》《星島足球》

Michael Jackson 逝世

2009·06· 27
星期六
己丑年閏五月初五日
港幣六元正
今天出紙3疊16張半
報網一體

女嬰營養不良死 父母被捕

The Jackson 5 were an immediate hit, their first single 'I Want You Back' reaching No 1 in the US, as did the next three. They were instantly popular with prepubescent girls both black and white, and 11-year-old Michael became an object of desire, his cute face and giant afro haircut appearing on magazine covers throughout the globe. The workload that the J5 accomplished in their early years was extraordinary – 13 albums between 1969 and 1975 – and when they weren't in the studio they were rehearsing, or on tour or attending classes with a private tutor. Michael, it is widely believed, longed for the normal childhood he lost, and this may explain the unconventional, childlike behaviour that characterised much of his later life.

1972 Michael embarked on a concurrent and equally successful solo career, which meant that his work schedule was even more onerous than before. It was while playing the scarecrow in the film The Wiz, a variation on *The Wizard Of Oz*, in 1978 that he met the producer and writer Quincy Jones with whom he would collaborate on his best known and most accomplished work. By this time he had split with his father and, along with the group – now known as The Jacksons – left Motown for Columbia Records.

It was soon abundantly clear that Michael was putting his major effort into his solo work. *Off The Wall*, released in 1979, heralded the arrival of a major solo star, but this was nothing compared to *Thriller* (1982). Seven of its nine tracks were massive hit singles, including a duet with Paul McCartney, and the album has gone on to become the biggest selling record ever, with sales generally estimated to be in the region of 65 million. It remained at number one in the US *Billboard* album charts for 37 weeks and won eight Grammy awards. The following year, at a televised gala for Motown Records 25th anniversary, Michael unveiled his moonwalk dance before a global audience. It would become his signature move, along with the single silver glove he wore on his right hand.

Michael Jackson's rise to world domination coincided with the emergence of the video as the principal means by which records were promoted, and the simultaneous appearance of MTV. At first the all-music TV channel was reluctant to show videos featuring coloured performers but Jackson changed all this with his lengthy video for the song 'Thriller' in which he metamorphosed from a charming young man into a ghoul-like zombie, his eyes sunk back into their sockets, his skeletal body leading a dancing troupe risen from the grave. This image of Michael Jackson, as seen on this and other videos from the mid-80s, is the image that most characterises the man, the remarkable talent that conquered the world.

The mid-'80s was the peak of Michael's career. As well as the videos there were era-defining concert shows in huge stadiums that broke new bounds for spectacle. His on-stage dancing was simply breathtaking and the special effects as dazzling as anything the entertainment world had ever seen. He performed conjuring tricks, seemingly appearing in two places at the same time, and, with a jet-pack strapped to his back, even flew over the heads of his audience. He dressed in clothes that were almost always a variation of embroidered red and black military wear, the kind of dress uniforms preferred by African dictators. He wore them off stage too, as if his life was a constant performance.

The final record in the Quincy Jones trilogy, *Bad* (1987), was the first album ever to produce five US No.1 hits. Though it failed to sell as many copies as *Thriller*, it solidified Michael's position as the biggest solo act on the planet, and by this time he had awarded himself the title The King Of Pop. Ominously, press releases issued by his record label instructed magazine editors always to refer to Michael in these terms.

All this success was inevitably accompanied by much intrusive reportage concerning his personal welfare and private life. His appearance had changed considerably from the cute little African American boy who fronted the J5. Michael's hair was now straight, his nose sharply pointed and, most remarkably, his skin appeared to be getting lighter. He married – and divorced – Lisa Marie Presley, the daughter of Elvis, and married a second time to Debbie Rowe, a nurse who produced his two children, a boy Prince Michael, and a girl Paris, before they separated. A third child, Prince Michael II, was born to a surrogate mother, identity unknown.

As if all this wasn't enough Michael's behaviour became increasingly erratic as the '90s progressed. He was rarely seen in public without a face-mask and was reputed to sleep in a specially-built oxygen chamber designed to prolong his life. Minders who surrounded him invariably carried umbrellas to protect him from sunlight. He lived on a ranch near Los Angeles called Neverland, named after the mythical kingdom in J. M. Barrie's fantasy Peter Pan, where children never grow up. He had his own private zoo and theme park, complete with fairground rides. His best friend was a chimpanzee named Bubbles.

this behaviour was seen by most as mere eccentricity, typical of Hollywood showbiz elite, more
inister were charges of child molestation brought in 1993 by a 13-year-old boy. The case was dropped
mid rumours of an out-of-court settlement of anything up to $25 million. A second, far more
amaging, child-abuse case was brought against him in 2003 and although Michael was acquitted of
e charges, by this time he was without doubt the world's No 1 showbiz weirdo, now universally
nown in the press as Wacko Jacko.

eanwhile, Michael's financial affairs were coming under scrutiny. His earnings from *Thriller* alone
ould have been sufficient to bankroll the economy of a small country but his lavish spending was
ating into his fortune at an alarming rate. Along the way he'd purchased for a sum believed to be
47 million a controlling interest in ATV Music which gave him the rights to Northern Songs, the
eatles' song publishing catalogue. This caused a cooling in his relationship with Paul McCartney who,
was later revealed, had actually once advised Michael to invest his massive earnings in music
ublishing. By the turn of the century he'd sold part of his interest in ATV to Sony, and was rumoured
be in debt to the tune of $270 million.

As Michael's life unravelled during the 90s and in the early years of the 21st century, his record sales were dropping off alarmingly. The 'best of' album *HIStory* did well but *Invincible* (2001), his last album of original material, was a critical and commercial disappointment. In 2004 it was reported that his next album would be financed by his friend Sheik Abdullah of Bahrain, who would co-write the songs, but the pair fell out and the Sheik sued Jackson in an attempt to recover his money. This album, if it exists remains unreleased.

By his standards, Michael kept a low-profile in recent years but he broke cover early in 2009 to announce that he would perform a staggering and unprecedented 50 shows at the O2 Arena in London. The concerts, he said, would be his last ever. Many commentators were unconvinced the shows would actually happen but no-one can have guessed that the reason for their cancellation would be Michael's sudden death, evidently from a heart attack, on 25 June.

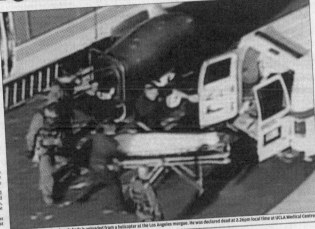

he day after the show at the Talk Of The Town I was invited to a press reception for Michael and

s brothers at the Churchill Hotel in Portman Square. The whereabouts of the group had become

nown and outside in the square a line of policemen held back agitated fans who screamed loudly and

oked upon me with deep envy as I flashed my invitation and was allowed through the barriers.

side the hotel, in a private suite on the ground floor, Jackie, Tito, Jermaine, Marlon and Michael sat

: tables where journalists could speak briefly to them before being moved on to the next brother.

hen it came to my turn to talk to Michael he looked up from his comic book, smiled graciously but

aid very little. For want of anything better, I asked him how he liked London. "London's great," he said

uietly, then looked back down at his comic. I knew immediately that an in-depth interview was

npossible.

en, as ever, he was in a world of his own.

BABY BE MINE

Words & Music by Rod Temperton

1. I____ don't need no____ dreams____ when I'm by your side,____ oo.
2. I____ won't give you____ rea - son to change your mind.____ (I
3. There'll__ be no more moun - tains for us to climb.____ (I

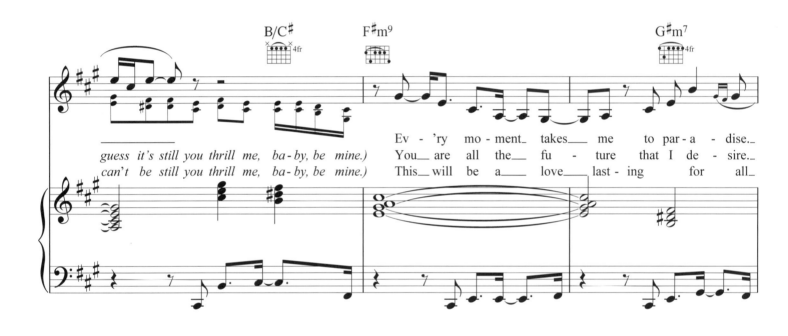

guess it's still you thrill me, ba-by, be mine.) Ev-'ry mo-ment_ takes__ me to par-a - dise.
can't be still you thrill me, ba-by, be mine.) You__ are all the__ fu - ture that I de - sire.
This__ will be a__ love__ last - ing for all__

____ time.
Dar-lin', let__ me hold you,
Girl, I need__ to hold you,
Girl, you got__ to hold me,

BLAME IT ON THE BOOGIE

Words & Music by Elmar Krohn, Thomas Meyer, Hans Kampschroer,
Michael Jackson Clark & David Jackson Rich

29

BURN THIS DISCO OUT

Words & Music by Rod Temperton

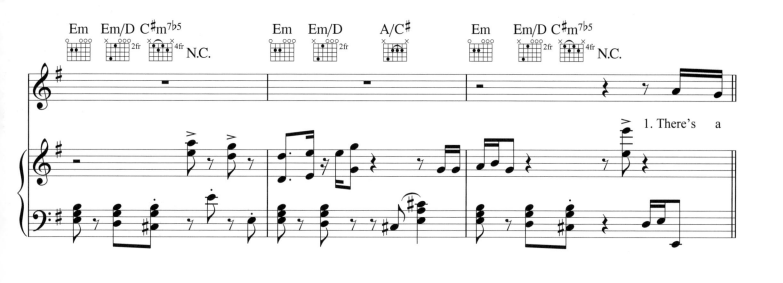

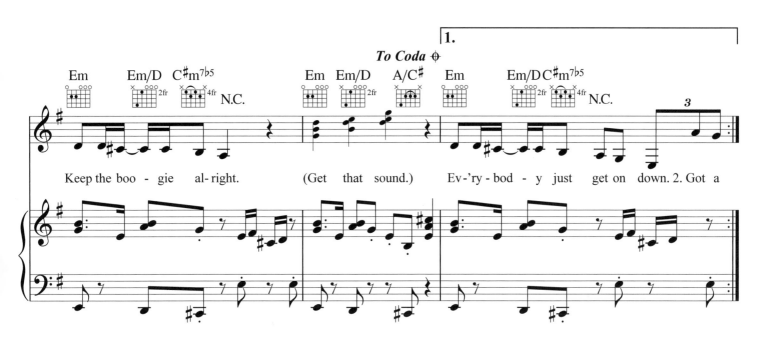

Keep the boo - gie al - right. (Get that sound.) Ev-'ry - bod - y just get on down. 2. Got a

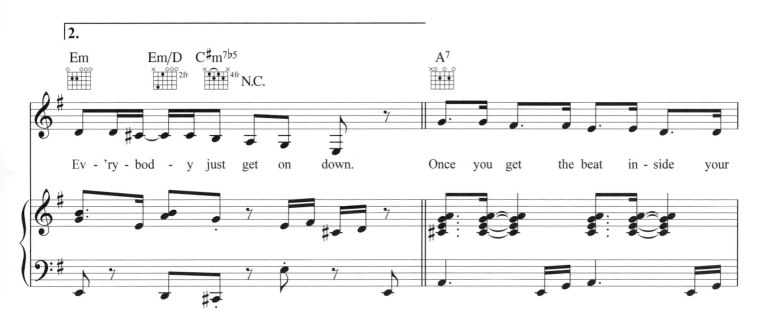

Ev - 'ry - bod - y just get on down. Once you get the beat in - side your

feet, there ain't no way to stop you mov - in' good.___

Now the week-end's come, it's time for fun, you got to groove just like you know   you should.__

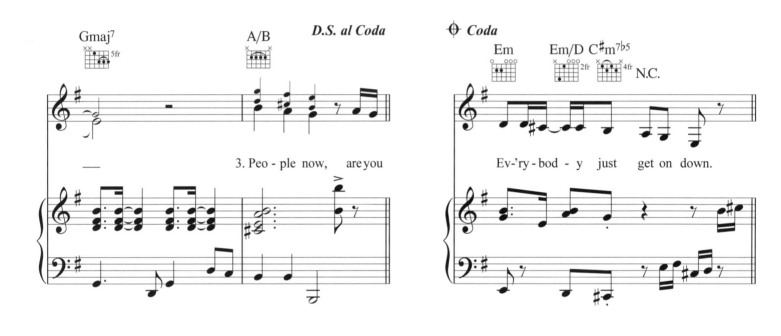

D.S. al Coda

Coda

3. Peo - ple now,   are you

Ev-'ry-bod - y   just   get on down.

burn this dis - co_____ out.____ Keep the boo - gie al - right. Gon-na
(Groove all night.)

dance, gon-na shout, gon-na burn this dis - co out.
(Get that sound.)

Repeat to fade

Ev -'ry-bod - y get down to-night. Gon-na dance, gon-na shout, gon-na burn this dis - co

38

CAN YOU FEEL IT

Words & Music by Michael Jackson & Jackie Jackson

45

you take / do shine   is some-one's death in an-oth-er place.   Mm.__
and prom-ise and sal-va-tion is near this time.

Ev-'ry breath

CRY

Words & Music by R. Kelly

1. Some-bod-y shakes when the wind
2. Peo-ple laugh when they're feel-

blows.
-ing sad.

Some-bod-y's miss-ing a friend.___ Hold on.
Some-one is tak-ing a life.___ Hold on.

Some-bod-y's lack-ing a he - ro.___ And they have not a clue___ when it's
re-spect to be-lieve in your dreams.___ So tell me where were you___ when your

50

GIRLFRIEND

Words & Music by Paul McCartney

1. Girl - friend,__ I'm gon - na tell your boy - friend,__ yeah.__
2. Girl - friend,__ I'm gon - na show your boy - friend,__ yeah.__
3. Girl - friend,__ you bet - ter tell your boy - friend,__ yeah.__

HUMAN NATURE

Words & Music by Steve Porcaro & John Bettis

1.Look-ing out__ 'cross__ the night-time, the cit-y winks a sleep-less

(funky 'off-beat' feel throughout)

do me that way? If they_ say why, why, da-da-da-da-da-da-da-da,

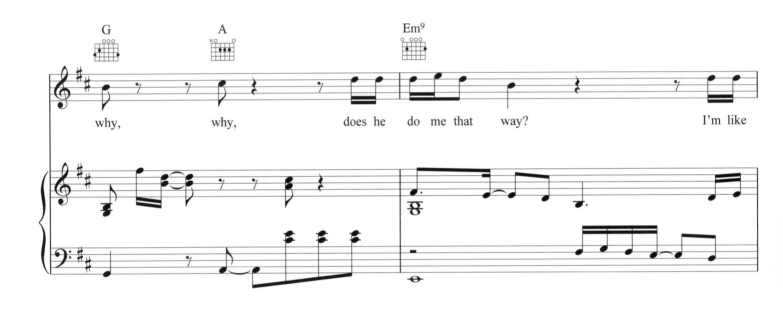

why, why, why, does he do me that way? I'm like

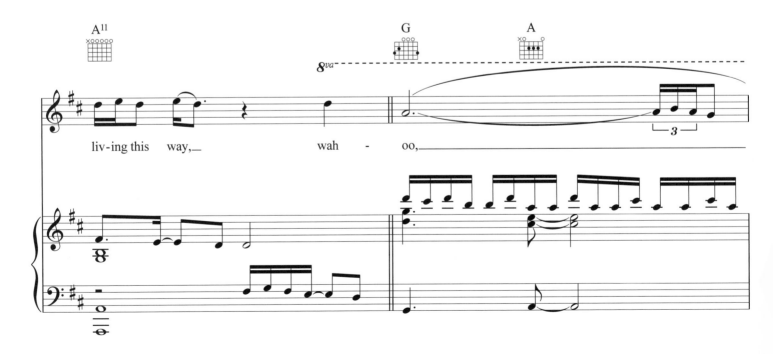

liv-ing this way,_ wah-oo,_

Repeat to fade

THE LADY IN MY LIFE

Words & Music by Rod Temperton

Soul Ballad ♩ = 73

1. There'll be no dark-ness to - night,___ la - dy our love___ will shine.___

77

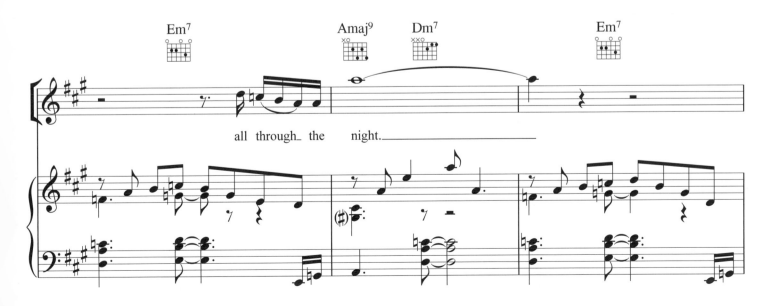

MAN IN THE MIRROR

Words & Music by Glen Ballard & Siedah Garrett

OFF THE WALL

Words & Music by Rod Temperton

1. When the world is on your shoul - der,_____ got - ta
(2.) shout out all you want to,_____ 'cause there

straight-en up your act and boog-ie down._____ If you can't hang with the feel - ing,_____
ain't no sin in folks all get-tin' loud._____ If you take the chance and do it,_____

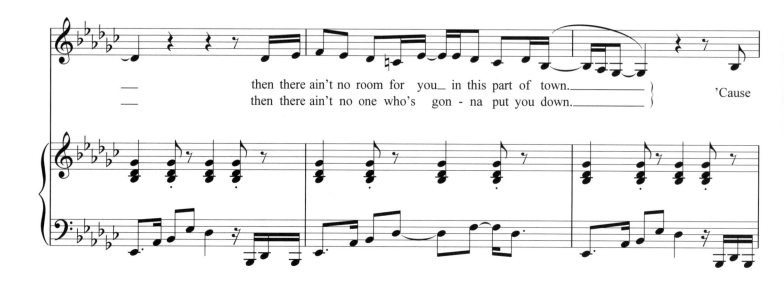

then there ain't no room for you__ in this part of town.____ 'Cause
then there ain't no one who's gon - na put you down.____

we're the__ par - ty peo - ple night and__ day,____ liv - in'__ cra - zy, that's the

on - ly__ way.__ So,__ to - night,____ got - ta leave that nine - to - five__ up - on the shelf,__

got-ta leave that nine-to-five_ up-on the shelf,___ and just en-

-joy your - selves.___ Groove, let the mad-ness in the mu - sic get to you,_

Repeat to fade

life ain't so bad at___ all,_____ To -

ONE MORE CHANCE

Words & Music by R. Kelly

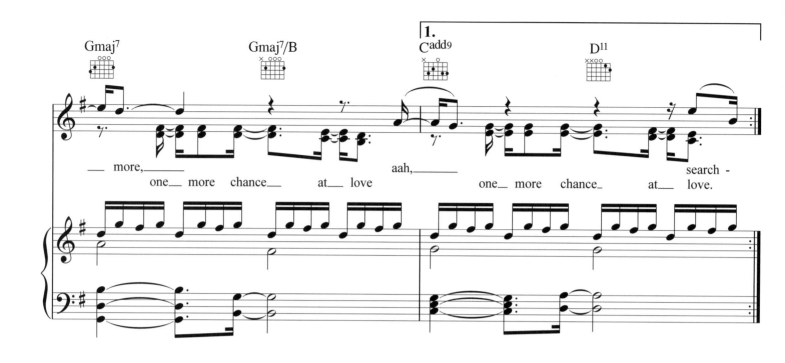

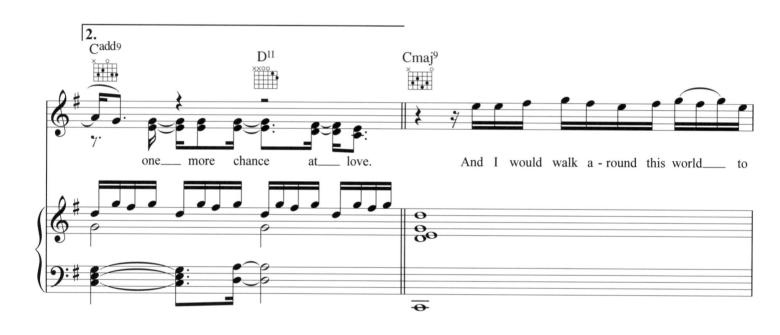

I'd sail the sev-en seas to be near her,_____ and if you

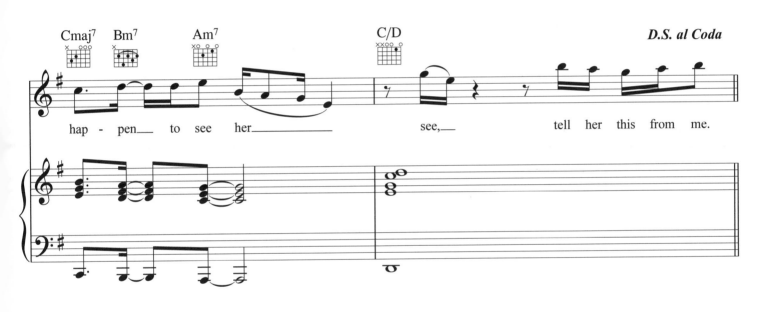

hap-pen__ to see her_____ see,__ tell her this from me.

D.S. al Coda

one__ more chance__ at__ love one__ more chance__ at__ love. One____

P.Y.T.(PRETTY YOUNG THING)

Words & Music by Quincy Jones & James Ingram

1. Where did you come___from la - dy, and ooh, won't you take me there?
2. Noth - ing can stop___this burn - ing de - si - re to be with you.

112

ROCK WITH YOU

Words & Music by Rod Temperton

1. Girl,___ close your eyes, let that rhy-thm get in - to you.
2. Out on the floor there ain't no - bod - y there but us.

(I wan - na rock with you,   I wan - na groove with you.)

(I wan - na rock with you,   I wan - na groove. with you.)_

I wan - na

ROCKIN' ROBIN

Words & Music by Jimmie Thomas

Pret-ty lit-tle ra-ven at the bird band-stand, taught__ him how to do the bop and

it was grand. They start-ed go-in' stea-dy and a - bless my soul, he

out - bopped the buz-zard and the o - ri - ole!____ He

D.S. al Coda I

THRILLER

Words & Music by Rod Temperton

1. It's close to mid - night,___ and some-thin' e - vil's lurk - in' in the dark.___
2. You hear the door___ slam___ and re - al - ize there's no-where left to run.___
3. They're out to get___ you. There's de - mons clos - in' in on ev-'ry-side.___

Un - der the moon - light___ you
You feel the cold___ hand, and
They will pos-sess___ you un-

I'm gon-na thrill you to -

C#m **A/C#** **B/C#** **F#/C#** *Repeat ad lib. to fade*

-night. *(See spoken lyrics)*

Spoken lyrics:
Darkness falls across the land
The midnight hour is close at hand
Creatures crawl in search of blood
To terrorize y'all's neighbourhood
And whosoever shall be found
Without the soul for getting down
Must stand and face the hounds of hell
And rot inside a corpse's shell.

The foulest stench is in the air
The funk of forty thousand years
And grizzly ghouls from every tomb
Are closing in to seal your doom
And though you fight to stay alive
Your body starts to shiver
For no mere mortal can resist
The evil of the thriller.

YOU ARE NOT ALONE

Words & Music by R. Kelly

Verse 2
You are not alone
I am here with you
Though you're far away
I am here to stay.
You are not alone
I am here with you
Though we're far apart
You're always in my heart.
But you are not alone.

Verse 3
Just the other night
I thought I heard you cry
Asking me to go
And hold you in my arms.
I can hear your breaths
Your burdens I will bear
But first I need you here
Then forever can begin.

Verse 4
You are not alone
 I am here with you
Though you're far away
I am here to stay.
But you are not alone
I am here with you
Though we're far apart
You're always in my heart.
But you are not alone.

1 2 3 4 5 6 7 8 9

MICHAEL JACKSON
1958-2009

Published by
Wise Publications
14-15 Berners Street, London, W1T 3LJ, UK.

Exclusive distributors:
Music Sales Limited
Distribution Centre,
Newmarket Road, Bury St Edmunds, Suffolk, IP33 3YB, UK.
Music Sales Pty Limited
20 Resolution Drive, Caringbah, NSW 2229, Australia.

Order No. AM998613
ISBN 978-1-84938-256-4

Compiled by Nick Crispin.
Edited by Jenni Wheeler.
Music processed by Paul Ewers Music Design.
Photo research by Jacqui Black.
Photographs by...
Cover image: Matthew Rolston/Corbis Outline.
Inside front cover: LFI. Pages 4 & 5: LFI. Page 6: LFI.
Page 7: LFI & Corbis. Pages 8 & 9: LFI & Kevin Mazur/Getty Images.
Pages 10 & 11: Sipa Press/Rex Images, Epic, Idols.
Page 12: Kevin Mazur/Getty Images. Page 14: Lynn Goldsmith/Corbis.
Page 24: Hulton – Deutsch Collection/Corbis. Page 31: Redferns.
Page 39: Redferns. Page 48: WireImage. Page 54: Redferns.
Page 60: Jacqueline Sallow/Corbis. Page 70: Jeff Slocombe/Sygma/Corbis.
Page 81: WireImage. Page 89: Redferns.
Page 98: John G. Mabanglo/epa/Corbis. Page 105: Bettman/Corbis.
Page 114: Getty Images. Page 121: Getty Images.
Page 128: Epic. Page 136: Getty Images.
Inside back cover: Michael Johansson/Idols.

Printed in the EU.

www.musicsales.com